The catch

Saturday was going to be Open Day at St Joseph's Primary School. In the morning the parents could talk to the teachers and look at the children's work. Afterwards the sports would start, followed by a picnic lunch and a jumble sale. The top two classes were going to have a rounders match.

'I hope it doesn't rain like last year,' said Dad.

'So do I,' said Laura. 'I'm going to be captain of our rounders team.'

'I wish I could do sports,' said Ben.

'You will, one day,' Dad replied.

It wasn't going to be a proper rounders match. It was a bit like rounders and a bit like baseball. Some of the rules had been changed by the teachers. One rule said that the teams had to wear fancy dress. The best fancy dress got a prize, and that was all part of the fun, but the children took the match very seriously indeed.

On Friday evening Laura and Ben were in the garden practising rounders. They couldn't do much more than practise catching the ball because Ben couldn't walk. Every time he missed the ball Laura had to go and pick it up.

'It's a pity your legs don't work,' said Laura. 'You catch better than I do.'

'I know,' said Ben. 'My aim is better, too.'

'Do you want to have a go with the bat?' asked Laura. 'I'm tired of catching.'

'We could have a go,' said Ben.

Laura pushed Ben to the top of the garden and handed him the rounders bat. 'I'll try an easy one first,' she thought. Ben hit the ball back to her.

'Too easy,' he said. 'Just because my legs don't work, it doesn't mean there's anything wrong with my arms.'

So Laura bowled him a difficult ball.

Ben gave the ball a terrific swipe. Laura ran to catch it, but it was moving too fast. The ball shot over her head and crashed through the window of the garden shed.

'I think that's enough practice for this evening,' said Dad, coming out of the shed.

On Saturday morning Dad put Ben's wheelchair in the boot of the car and strapped Ben into the back seat. Laura, as usual, wasn't ready. 'Where's my sports kit?' she grumbled.

'I've got it here,' said Dad. 'If it was up to you to remember everything, it would still be in your sports bag, covered in mud.'

On the way to school Dad stopped to pick up Maggie, Laura's best friend. The girls were very excited but Ben seemed miserable.

'What's the matter, Ben?' asked Maggie. 'Aren't you looking forward to the sports?'

'No I'm not,' said Ben. 'I get miserable when I see everybody running about. I want to join in.'

When they got to St Joseph's, Laura went to change into her sports kit. Miss Kelly helped Dad put Ben into his chair. 'Why are you looking so miserable today, Ben?' she asked.

'It's no fun just watching,' said Ben.

'Nonsense!' laughed Miss Kelly. 'You're going to have a lovely day. There will be all sorts of things for you to do. We can't have anybody being miserable on a fine, sunny day like this.'

Ben cheered up a little when he saw the stalls and sideshows. Miss Kelly pushed him around the field while Dad went to see Laura's teacher.

Soon it was time for the races. The first one was to be the three-legged race. Dad pushed Ben to watch the start. The teachers found it hard work to keep the children in order.

Miss Kelly came up to Dad and Ben. 'I've got a problem,' she said. 'I have to go and stand at the finishing post, so I've got nobody to start the races. Will you be the starter, Ben?'

'Does that mean I have to blow the whistle?' gasped Ben.

'Better than that,' laughed Miss Kelly. 'We've got a starting pistol. I'll put your Dad in charge of the pistol, but you can start the races.'

She pinned a badge on Ben's jacket. It said 'Starter' in big red letters.

Everybody was waiting for Ben. 'I hope I do this right,' he whispered.

'Just point it in the air, and when everybody is ready, pull the trigger. Then give it back to me,' said Dad.

Ben felt very proud and important. The children were ready. Ben pointed the pistol in the air and pulled the trigger. There was a terrific bang.
It's hard to run when your leg is tied to somebody else's and most of the children fell over because they were laughing so much.

For the rest of the morning Ben enjoyed himself. He started all the races. 'This isn't so bad after all,' he said.

'We couldn't have managed without you,' said Dad.

After the races came the picnic. The teachers and parents had made hundreds of sandwiches and cakes. There was tea for the grown-ups and orange juice for the children. The picnic was the part of the day Maggie liked best.

'If you eat any more of those sandwiches you won't be able to play rounders,' warned Laura.

'I've only eaten eight,' said Maggie, helping herself to a cake.

'Nine!' said Ben. 'And two ice-creams!'

Miss Kelly took Ben round the stalls.

'Can I have a go on the darts, please?' he asked.

'Of course,' said Miss Kelly. 'I'll have a go too.' Miss Kelly wasn't much good at darts, but Ben won three times which meant he could choose a prize.

'What about that football?' asked Miss Kelly. Ben laughed. 'I'd have to win some proper legs to go with it,' he said. In the end he chose a game of snakes and ladders.

It was time for the rounders match. Miss Kelly set out the posts and Mr Drury fetched the bat and ball. The two teams were in the changing room putting on fancy dress.

Maggie began to clutch her tummy and groan. 'Oh no!' said Laura. 'What's the matter with you?'

'Too much picnic,' wailed Maggie. 'I think I'm going to be ill.'

'But you can't!' gasped Laura. 'The match is about to begin.'

'Come on everybody,' said Miss Kelly. 'We're waiting to start.'

'I feel sick, Miss,' said Maggie. 'I don't think I'll be able to play.'

'Oh no!' said Laura. 'That means we'll be a person short in my team.'

'You'll just have to find a substitute,' said Miss Kelly. 'Why don't you ask Ben to take Maggie's place? I'm sure he'd enjoy the game.'

'But he can't run!' gasped Laura. 'And he hasn't got fancy dress. The rule is fancy dress.'

'He can bat, though,' said Miss Kelly, 'and we can find somebody to run for him.'

'I'll do that,' said Father O'Leary, who had been listening. 'I haven't had a good run for years. I may be able to help with the fancy dress, too.'

Laura's team batted first. When it was his turn, Ben was pushed on to the field wearing Father O'Leary's collar and a black T-shirt. Everybody clapped and cheered. Ben saw Dad roaring with laughter.

Avta Singh was getting ready to throw the ball.

'There's no need to make it easy,' called Ben. 'I've done this before.'

Avta bowled a fast one to Ben but it went wide.

'Wide!' yelled Mr Drury who was referee. The next ball was slower. Ben watched it curve towards him. Then he brought down his bat and gave the ball a terrific swipe. It sailed over the heads of the crowd and out of the playground.

'Run!' yelled Ben. Father O'Leary ran. He passed the first post, and the second, and the third.

'Faster!' yelled Ben. Father O'Leary passed the last post just as the ball was thrown back.

'We did it!' shouted Ben. 'We got a rounder!' Everybody jumped up and down. 'Well done, Ben!' they all shouted.

Laura's team batted very well but at last they were all out. 'That was the best fun I've had all week,' said Father O'Leary, 'but I need a bit of a rest.'

'I'm not going to be able to field,' said Ben, 'so I'll watch the rest from the sidelines.'

Laura's team fielded well. It was almost the end of the game and the scores were even. There was only one player left to bat. She was dressed as a duck. She had already run two rounders and needed one more to even the score.

The crowd was very quiet as Laura threw the ball.

The duck gave the ball a terrific swipe, and ran for the first post. The ball rose into the air.

Higher and higher went the ball. Then it began to fall. The duck had almost reached the second post. Ben could see where the ball was going to land. It would be almost close enough to catch. The crowd was cheering and shouting as the duck ran for the third post.

'If only . . . ' Ben began to move his wheelchair towards the ball. He turned the wheels faster and faster. Parents, teachers, and children saw what was happening and held their breath. Ben's arms were pushing as hard as they could. The ball was falling fast now.

At the last moment Ben threw himself forward.

The wheelchair overbalanced and Ben fell out. Mr Drury and Miss Kelly ran towards him. So did Dad, Laura, and the duck.

Ben wasn't hurt. He sat up, with a big smile on his face, and held up the ball.

'He caught it!' yelled Laura. 'We've won!'

Everybody started laughing and cheering and rushing forward to congratulate Ben.

The duck was out, but she was very sporting about it. 'I wish you'd been on our team, Ben,' she said. 'I've never seen a catch like that.'

'At least you weren't out for a duck,' said Ben.

Chinese horoscopes

The Chinese say that the year in which you are born affects the way you are, and the way you behave. Each year is ruled by one of twelve animals.

The Rat

People born in the year of the rat are cheerful, make friends easily, and like to save money.

The Ox

Those born in the year of the ox are healthy, strong and quiet. They finish everything they start but can be stubborn at times.

丑

寅

The Tiger

Tigers are strong and brave. They make good leaders and love to solve difficult problems.

The Rabbit

People born in the year of the rabbit like beautiful things. They are lucky and successful and they have a lot of patience. Like real rabbits they are often shy.

The Dragon

Dragons are proud people. They are healthy, brave and have lots of energy. They are honest, reliable, and good leaders.

The Snake

Snakes are wise and gentle. Because they are good-looking they are often proud. They work hard and usually grow rich.

The Horse

People born in the year of the horse are cheerful and intelligent. They are strong, and like hard work. They also like having fun.

The Goat

Goats are likeable people. They are often rich and like good things, especially good food. They can't make up their minds and like to complain.

The Monkey

Jokes and mischief are what monkeys like best. They want to know everything and never seem to stop talking. They have good imaginations and are very good at sums.

The Chicken
Chickens are clever and brave and enjoy competition. They don't mind their own business and often upset their friends. They're very fond of music.

The Dog
You can always trust a dog. Dogs are helpful and loyal. They are very reliable people and look after their families.

The Pig
It's good to be a pig. Pigs are kind, honest, and good-looking. They are never afraid to say what they think. Best of all, they like giving parties.

What are you?

1972	Rat	1978	Horse	1984	Rat	1990	Horse
1973	Ox	1979	Goat	1985	Ox	1991	Goat
1974	Tiger	1980	Monkey	1986	Tiger	1992	Monkey
1975	Rabbit	1981	Chicken	1987	Rabbit	1993	Chicken
1976	Dragon	1982	Dog	1988	Dragon	1994	Dog
1977	Snake	1983	Pig	1989	Snake	1995	Pig

Remember that the Chinese New Year doesn't start until the end of January. So if you were born in January 1981, for example, you would still be a monkey.

The race

Long ago, when the world was fresh and new, the gods lived high up in the sky. They walked upon pathways through the clouds as easily as we human beings walk upon leaves in the forest.

Under the clouds lay the Earth. The Jade Emperor was ruler of the gods and lord of the Heavens and Earth. He sent the sun to warm the land, and gentle rain to water it.

The land was full of animals, birds, and insects. The gods took care of the Earth and the creatures that lived upon it.

For a long time all creatures on Earth were happy. The gods thought that because the animals had plenty to eat, and a beautiful world to enjoy, they would live in peace with each other for ever.

One day The Jade Emperor decided to visit the creatures on the Earth. As the sun rose in the Heavens he looked down from the cloud on which he was sitting. He saw the white snow upon the mountain tops turn pink as the day dawned. The sweet scents of the forest filled his nostrils, and he listened with delight to the breeze playing in the rice fields. He watched the silver fish leaping in the river and smiled. 'All is well,' he thought.

As the sun began to warm the Earth, the creatures that lived in the forests and in the rice fields began to wake up. A terrible noise caused The Jade Emperor to cover his ears. It was the sound of animal voices, raised in anger. They were all arguing about which of them was the most important.

'I should be ruler over all of you,' said the tiger. 'I'm the bravest.'

'I should be ruler,' snapped the monkey. 'I'm cleverer than any of you.'

'It should be me,' said the rabbit. 'There are more rabbits than any other animal.'

'Me!' hissed the snake.

'Me!' roared the dragon.

'Me!' grunted the pig. And so it went on until The Jade Emperor could stand no more of it, and hurried back across the clouds to his Jade Palace.

The Jade Emperor sent for all the gods. 'We must settle this argument,' he said. 'We shall have a race to decide which animal shall be king over the others. Some of you will go down to Earth and invite them all to take part. I shall decide where the race shall be run.'

The next day twelve animals came to the foot of the tallest mountain. They were the tiger, the rabbit, the horse, the goat, the monkey, the chicken, the rat, the ox, the dog, the pig, the snake, and the dragon. The Emperor's servant told them where the race was to be run. 'First you must run through the forest,' he said. 'Then you must cross the rice fields. Finally you must swim the great river. The first animal to reach the far bank will be the winner, and rule over you all.'

When the animals were all lined up, The Jade Emperor nodded to his servant, and the servant shouted 'Go!' The Emperor and all the gods walked across the clouds to see the finish.

The forest was difficult for the big animals but the little ones darted between the trees easily and were soon in the lead. The chicken flew above them all and the monkey laughed as he jumped from branch to branch.

When they came to the rice fields it was the smaller creatures who had problems. The powerful animals, the horse, the ox, and the tiger, began to catch up. By the time they reached the river bank they were all equal, but they were all very tired.

The river was difficult for all of them. The chicken was too tired to fly, and the dog, the tiger and the horse were poor swimmers in such a strong current. The best swimmer was the ox and he gradually began to overtake the rat, who had been in the lead. The rat was very cunning. As the ox swam past him, the rat jumped on to the ox's back. When the ox had almost reached the bank the rat jumped from his back on to the land. 'I won! I won!' he squeaked.

'Cheat!' bellowed the ox as he scrambled out of the water. 'I'm the real winner!' As the other animals reached the finish they all began to join in the argument.

'Silence!' ordered the Emperor's servant. 'The Jade Emperor himself will decide who is the winner.'

When the animals were quiet, The Jade Emperor came down from his cloud and spoke to them. 'Twelve of you entered the race,' he said, 'and though the rat was first to the bank you shall all be winners. You shall each take it in turns to rule for a year. The rat will be first and at the end of the year, he will hand over his power to the ox. When the twelve years are complete the rat will start again and you will all follow, in the same order, for ever.'

As the god finished speaking, the lion came running up. 'Am I too late for the race?' he asked.

'Yes,' replied the Emperor. 'There are no years left for you to rule. I have made a decision and I can't change my mind now. However, at the end of each old year there shall be a great procession, and you, Lion, shall have the honour of leading it.'

The gods went back to their homes in the skies, and the animals, pleased with the decision of The Jade Emperor, made friends and lived in happiness.